G000245696

Fish-it 9
Cornwall

Produced By: Chris Keeling

Published by:
**Arc Publishing and Print
166 Knowle Lane
Bents Green
Sheffield
S11 9SJ**

Text copyright 2014 © Chris Keeling

The rights of Chris Keeling and his work have been asserted by him in
accordance with the
Copyright, Design Patent Act 1988

Whilst every effort has been made to ensure the contents of this
publication are accurate at the time of publishing.
Arc Publishing and Print and those involved in producing the content
of "Fish-it 9" cannot be held responsible for any errors, omissions or
changes in the details of this guide or for the consequences of any
reliance on the information provided in it. We have tried to ensure
accuracy in this guide but things do change and we would be grateful
if readers could advise us of any inaccuracies they have found.

ISBN: 978-1-906722-32-6

ACKNOWLEDGEMENTS

I would like to thank the following for their
help in producing this guide:

Cornwall-online.co.uk (Fishing in Cornwall)

South West Lakes Trust

Westcountry Angling

Thank you to all fishery owners who kindly provided information

and to those that gave permission to use

images from their websites.

I have tried to ensure the accuracy of this guide but things do change
very quickly so if you know of any inaccuracies or any fisheries I have
not included I would be grateful if you could fill out and return the form
at the back of the guide.

April 2014

Arc Publishing and Print
166 Knowle Lane
Bents Green
Sheffield
S11 9SJ

W E L C O M E

I have visited Cornwall many times over the last few years for family holidays as well as fishing trips. Cornwall has always been a holiday destination, so I have included information about accommodation available plus camping and caravan facilities at many of the venues. Although Fish-it guides are normally for coarse fishing only, I couldn't ignore the many placed along the coast where the beach, rock and sea fishing is excellent.

Like many other anglers, my time on the bank is limited, but I like to grab a few hours fishing whenever and wherever I can.
Bearing this in mind, I have put together this edition of 'Fish-it Cornwall' with details of some of the best day ticket and holiday park waters in the area. Each page has all the details you need to choose a venue that suits your method of fishing. It will give you an idea of what the fishery is like before setting off on a lengthy (and now with petrol prices so high) expensive journey.

Fishing attracts so many people. Perhaps it is the solitude in often beautiful surroundings. Of course there is also the eager anticipation of catching the big one! The bankside can be almost hypnotic and the desire to catch just one more fish has spoilt many a meal.

I hope you find this book useful and wish you good luck, good fishing and remember -
"A bad day's fishing is still better than a good day's work!"

Chris Keeling

C O N T E N T S

ABOUT THIS GUIDE

To help you locate a fishery, the venues have been arranged in alphabetical order and split into two sections, fisheries and rivers. Their approximate location has been indicated on a map on page 9.

fisheries and Rivers

Each page contains details of a fishery, with information on the following:

Ticket Price: All day ticket costs plus details on OAPs, disabled and junior concessions.

Directions: Usually from the nearest city or town, or from the closest motorway junction.

Description: A brief outline of what the fishery looks like plus details on features such as islands, depths and the best places to fish.

Types of Fish: List of species present, many with estimated weights.

Rules/Bans: The restrictions set by the fishery on type of baits, hooks etc.

Number of Lakes: The number of waters available to fish at the venue.

Facilities: What is available at each location i.e. cafe.

Accommodation: Information on holiday accommodation available for hire at each location

Telephone: The number of either the owner, angling club secretary or match organiser.

Sat Nav: Post Codes for use on satellite navigation systems.

S P E C I E S / S Y M B O L S

Coarse fish most commonly found in the Cornwall area.

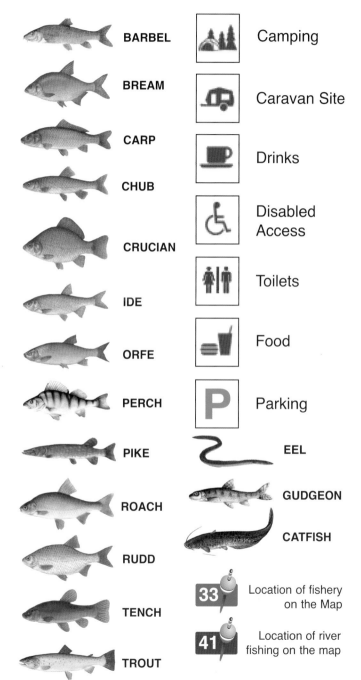

BARBEL

Camping

BREAM

Caravan Site

CARP

Drinks

CHUB

Disabled Access

CRUCIAN

IDE

Toilets

ORFE

Food

PERCH

Parking

PIKE

EEL

ROACH

GUDGEON

RUDD

CATFISH

TENCH

33 Location of fishery on the Map

41 Location of river fishing on the map

TROUT

Rock Fishing

There are many places where good rock fishing can be found on the coast of Cornwall, with an abundance of different species for the keen angler.

North Coast:
Good marks for ray and turbot are Trenance and Trevose where good quality pollock, mackerel, wrasse, garfish, plaice, dabs and conger can also be found.

Park Head is well known for a wonderful variety including gurnard, ray, pollock and wrasse.

Rumps Point to the east of Padstow for gurnard, ray, pollock and wrasse. Daymer Bay and the wave cut platforms at Pentire are both good marks but require caution.

Godrevy Point offers mackerel, pollock and wrasse, which are also plentiful at Navax Point. Rumps Point at St Agnes for gurnard, ray, plaice and dabs.

West Coast:
Prussia Cove and Cudden Point are good marks at night for mackerel and conger.

Penlee Point between Newlyn and Mousehole provides record catches. The areas between Mousehole and Lamorna, Penzer Point and Carn Du are also favourite marks.

Penberth Cove, Logan Rock and the rocks below the Minack Theatre are also great spots to try.

Pedn-men-an-mere, Porth Chapel, Porthgwarra and Mill Bay, near Land's End offer good sport.

The cliffs to the west of St Ives are for the experts only, access to the marks here involving a steep climb sometimes with the aid of a rope.

Aire Point, Cape Cornwall, Portheras, Clodgy Point and Man's Head can give good sport.

South Coast:
Good rock marks abound from Pendennis Point to Penhale. Those mentioned all require care.

Pendennis Point is a good mark for wrasse and pollock, as is St Anthony's Head which on autumnal nights is an excellent mark for black bream.

Porthallow offers good marks for coalfish and conger.

A superb mark for night fishing are both the Lizard and Trewavas Head where wrasse, mackerel and conger are good sport.

South East Coast:
Good rock fishing from Gribbin Head (long walk from car park), Black Head, Maenease Point, Goran Haven and Pencarrow. Rame Head. Queener Point in Whitsand Bay

Special care must be taken.

Beach Fishing

It should be noted that in summer the beaches are very popular with bathers and holidaymakers so beach and times should be chosen with some care.

North Coast:

The Bude breakwater and Crackington Haven are good marks for codling, flat fish, mackerel, whiting and dogfish. Widemouth Bay also offers good fishing.

Crooklets, Maer and Northcott Mouth are good beaches fished at two hours before low water and on the incoming tide, mostly for skate and flatfish.

Perranporth offers several miles of good beach for all flatfish as does Holywell Bay and Crantock. Watergate Bay is fine for ray, turbot and plaice as is Mawgan Porth and Constantine.

Chapel Porth is good for ray and turbot. Perranporth Beach is also popular with holidaymakers so avoid busy times: late evenings and early mornings will give excellent sport.

West Coast:

Perran Sands and Eastern Green Beach near Marazion offer flatfish and ray.

The piers and dock area of Penzance and Newlyn offer a wide variety of species with Lariggan Beach offering good flatfish after dark.

The pier at Lamorna, the niche between Porthcurno and Logan Rock, the beaches at Sennen offer flatfish, turbot, gurnard and dogfish.

The beaches at St Ives are crowded with holidaymakers during summer and all are best fished in the late evening and early morning.

South Coast:

The Prince of Wales Pier, Falmouth fishes well at night for pollock, mackerel and flounder.

Trefusis Point, Flushing for wrasse, pollock, mackerel and the occasional ray.

Coverack provides pollock, garfish and mackerel, try for conger and bull huss at the breakwater at night.

South East Coast:

Garfish, conger, mackerel, wrasse and pollack can all be caught from beaches in this area from Cawsand, Whitsand Bay, Seaton, Downderry, Plaidy Beach and Wallace Beach.

For flatfish try Par, Porthpean, Pentewan, Gorran Haven, Penare and Boswinger beaches. Early morning and late evening will avoid the bathers.

The docks at Par provide good jetty fishing, permit needed.

Sea Fishing

North Coast:
There is an abundance of charter boats available on the North Coast, particularly in Padstow, Port Isaac and Newquay.

West Coast:
On the West Coast boats are available from Penzance, Newlyn and St. Ives and offer a variety of options for the visiting sea angler.

South Coast:
In the South many chartered boats are available from Falmouth, particularly on Prince of Wales Pier and via the local tackle shops.

On the Roseland Peninsula, Mevagissey was once the fishing heart of the South Cornish coast. Mevagissey is the ideal spot from which to fish. Anglers can fish from the outer quay or use one of the self-hire boats for an hour.

Longer fishing trips are available on one of the many charter boats that sail from from Mevagissey harbour. An hours mackerel trip, a half day or whole day fishing - or cruising, taking in the scenery with a chance of seeing basking sharks, dolphins and seals. There is a fishing tackle shop called Mevagissey Angling Centre where you can book angling trips.

South East Coast:
Boats available in the South East, from Fowey and Looe.

Looe is fast becoming a household name for big game fishing for blue and portbeagle shark. Other marks fish well for ling, cod, bream and conger.

Looe in South East Cornwall, is an ideal spot for sea fishing, with Mackerel, Pilchard, Red and Grey Mullet, Pollack, Ling Coalfish, Cod, Sea Bass, Pouting, Wrasse, John Dory, Whiting Gurnard, Squid, Cuttlefish, Dogfish, Conger, Sharks (various species) all being caught in the local waters.

A number of boats offer Mackerel fishing trips from 2½ hours upwards, both during the day and early evening. These boats operate offshore in the bay, rods and bait provided.

Reef and Wreck fishing is available on the larger boats and Shark and Conger fishing commences at the beginning of June. The Sharks are tagged and released for conservation and scientific study.

Information kindly supplied by Cornwall-online.co.uk (Fishing in Cornwall)

COARSE FISHERY LOCATION MAP

Adamsfield Fishery

Tremaine, Launceston.

SAT NAV PL15 8UD

Ticket Price: Membership Only: Single member £55 per year. Retired / Concession £45 per year.
Family (2 adults and up to 4 children) £85 per year.

Directions: From Launceston take the A395. At Hallworthy head towards Warstow. Go through Warstow and turn right. Take your next left and look out for the fishery on your left hand side.

Description: Adamsfield Fishery is peacefully situated in the beautiful North Cornish countryside. It consists of over three and half acres of spring fed lakes that support a wide variety of coarse fish. The lakes are easily accessible and all the pegs are a generous size to enable the angler to set up equipment comfortably. On the lower match lake there is disabled access to two of the pegs. These pegs can be pre-booked if required. There is a good range of coarse fish, including mirror, crucian, ghost and common carp, tench, bream, golden rudd and some good sized perch. A good number of the carp are in double figures and provide for some exciting fishing. Carp are being caught with weights ranging from 1lb to 30lb.

Types of Fish:

Number of Lakes: Two

Rules/Bans: All fishermen must have a valid license. Please remember one licence covers 2 rods. No keep nets allowed unless in a competition. Ground bait in moderation. Barbless hooks to be used. Landing nets and mats to be used. All pegs to be left clean and tidy. Please use the bins for all rubbish. No dogs allowed except guide dogs.
Fishing is allowed between sunrise and sunset.

Facilities: ♿ 🚻 🅿 Telephone: 01566 781243
Sat Nav: PL15 8UD

Accommodation: Cabins available for holiday hire.

1 Fishery Location See page 9

Amalwhidden Farm

Amalwhidden Farm, Towednack, St. Ives.

SAT TR26 3AR NAV

Ticket Price: Adult day ticket (one rod) £5.00.
Adult day ticket (two rods) £7.00 (Heron Lake only)
Junior day ticket (one rod) £4.00 Junior day ticket (two rods)
£6.00 (Heron Lake only)
Evening ticket (After 3.00pm) £3.50 (Adults and Juniors)
Evening ticket (two rods after 3.00pm) £5.50
(Heron Lake only / Adults and Juniors)

Directions: From St. Ives take the B3306. Continue along this road for about 3 miles. Then turn left and follow the road through Towednack until you see the farm / fishery.

Description: Heron Lake is approximately 1.5 acres with 19 well spaced pegs and has a depth of 7-9 feet. It is well stocked with lots of mirror and common carp up to 11lb. It also has tench up to 2lbs, bream up to 3lbs, crucian carp and roach. Fir Tree Pond is approximate 1.25 acres with 17 pegs and a depth of 5-7 feet with a shallow stretch along one side of the main island. It's well stocked with mirror and common carp up to 5lbs, crucian carp, tench, bream and roach. It has two well planted islands which make interesting fish-holding features. Willow Pond is the smallest water but is packed with fish including a few ghost carp.

Types of Fish:

Rules/Bans: See on site for full listing.

Number of Lakes: Three

Facilities: Bait sold on site.
Fishing Rod Hire.
Beginners Fishing Tuition.

Accommodation: Farmhouse Self Catering Holidays.

Telephone: 01736 796961 / 07842 089760 **Sat Nav:** TR26 3AR

Bake Lakes

Bake Lakes Fishing, Trerulefoot, Saltash.

Ticket Price: Coarse lakes £7.00 per day. Specimen lake (Luxor) £8.50 per day. Under 12's free with paying adults.
Trout lakes - 2 fish ticket £17 / 3 fish £21 / 4 fish £25 / 5 fish £29

Directions: Leave the A38 at the exit signed 'Bake and Catchfrench' at Trerulefoot roundabout leaving the Route 38 Diner on the right. After 100 metres, turn right at the T-Junction. Continue for about ¼ mile and take the first left turn. The fishery entrance is 200 metres on the right, just past the entrance to Bake Farm on the left.

Description: Bake Lakes offers a wide variety of high quality angling opportunities and experiences from small 'silver fish' to giant, wily carp and "Fly Only" fishing for brown and rainbow trout. The fishery caters for all ages and levels of experience. The 9 lakes and ponds are situated in 30 acres of stunning, peaceful Cornish countryside. My favourite lake is Treasure Island, set in a steep sided valley, ideal for experts and families visiting the fishery. The lake holds carp into double figures, good tench and bream as well as a plentiful population of silver fish.

Types of Fish:

Rules/Bans: There are separate rules for trout fishing, coarse fishing and Luxor Lake which is the specimen lake. See details on site.

Number of Lakes: Nine   **Sat Nav:** PL12 5BW

Facilities:

Telephone: 07798 585836 or 01503 263349 (evenings only)

BK fisheries

The Green Lane, St. Erth, Nr Hayle.

Ticket Price: Adult Day Permit - 1 rod £7.00. 2 rods £10.00
Adult Night Permit - 2 rods - 12 noon till 12 noon £20.00
Junior Day Permit (up to 16 years) - 1 rod £6.00
Jnr Night Permit - 2 rods - 12 noon till 12 noon -- (must be accompanied by an ADULT) £18.00
Adult Evening Permit (after 5.00pm) 1 rod   £5.50
Junior Evening Permit (after 5.00pm) 1 rod   £4.50

Directions: Turn off the A30 at St. Erth Railway Station. Follow the road towards St. Erth. Turn right immediately after crossing river bridge. At St. Erth church follow narrow road for about 150 yards. Turn right into the fishery.

Description: Billys Pool is about 1.5 acres with depths that vary from 4 to 8 feet with the shallower water running down the middle of the lake. The lake is stuffed with hard fighting Cornish Carp and is literally foolproof. Whether you are experienced or not you will not fail to catch. Feeder, pole and waggler will all work well and you will catch fish a foot from the bank to the middle. Bills Pool is a mature, pretty lake of some 2.5 acres. Depths range from 5 to 18 feet in the middle. This lake contains large shoals of big bream, with a huge amount of silver fish and carp. Fish will take pellet, corn, worm, maggot or caster.

Types of Fish:

Number of Lakes: Two   **Rules/Bans:** See list on site.

Facilities: Tackle and fresh bait shop

Accommodation: None   **Sat Nav:** TR27 6HS

Telephone: 01736 753275 & 07919 130244

4
Fishery location
See page 9

Borlasevath

Borlasevath Manor Farm, St. Wenn, Bodmin.

Ticket Price: Day tickets £6.00 from the farmhouse. Under 14 year olds must be accompanied by an adult at all times.

Directions: From Bodmin take the A30 to Gossmore Bridge. Turn right onto the B3274 signposted Padstow. Continue for 3.5 miles, turn right at Tremayne Farm by a stone barn. You will find Borlasevath Manor Farm 1.25 miles on your left.

Description: There are five lakes to chose from at Borlasevath. They are of various sizes. The smallest is around half an acre, with the largest just over four acres. Set within farmland this peaceful fishery is perfect if you want a quite day. It's not unusual to have a lake to yourself. Carp reach 20lbs. and many of the smaller ones can be caught off the surface with bread crust or dog biscuit especially on a warm summer evening. Tench and bream go to 6.5lbs. and will take sweetcorn all day long. Maggot and caster will bag you plenty of good sized roach and rudd.

Types of Fish:

Rules/Bans: No carp to be retained in keepnets. Barbless hooks only. Fishing dawn till dusk only.

Number of Lakes: Five

Facilities: ♿ 🚻 🅿 Food outlet nearby.

Telephone: 07973 767147 **Sat Nav:** PL30 5PW

Coombe Mill

St. Breward, Bodmin.

Ticket Price: Free fishing is available all year round for the exclusive use of the guests.

Directions: From Exeter take the A30. After Launceston take A395 then the A39 to Camelford. After Camelford turn left on to the B3266 to Bodmin. After 3 miles turn left to St. Breward & Coombe Mill. Fork right to Coombe Mill. Take the next left to 'Coombe' and Penrose Burden. Drive down the hill to Coombe Mill.

Description: The lake is set within a family farm holiday site. There is a fishing lake and private river fishing along the banks of the River Camel. The Carp Lake is an extremely pretty spring fed lake that is sensitively managed to ensure the fish are healthy. It is well stocked with carp up to 20lbs. providing a tranquil backdrop for the holiday angler. The location is quiet and secluded yet close to the accommodation. As winter arrives so do the salmon that return up the river streaming past Coombe to provide challenging wild game fishing late into December. The sea trout season runs from 1 April to 30 September and the salmon season extends to 15 December.

Types of Fish:

Number of Lakes: One + a stretch of River Camel.

Facilities: **Sat Nav:** PL30 4LZ
Telephone: 01208 850344

Accommodation: Six Cottages, five Scandinavian Lodges, Six Riverside Lodges for holiday let.

Dutson Water

Lower Dutson Farm, Dutson, Launceston.

Ticket Price: £10 a day, on the bank. Fishing on the lake or on the River Tamar is free for guests staying at the cottages.

Directions: From Launceston, go south on Market Street and take the first left onto Southgate Street. Take the next left onto Angel Hill and left again onto the A388. Take the next right onto St. Thomas Road, staying on the A388. Take the 3rd exit at the roundabout onto Dutson Road. Go over the next roundabout and bear right. Look out for the farm on your left.

Description: An attractive tree shrouded lake with plenty of good sized fish. Each swim on this one acre lake is different with various depths and angles. It's stocked with mirror and common carp (some weighing over 20lb), tench, bream, perch, rudd and roach. There is no closed season and ample parking right by the water. Most carp tactics work but hair rigged large pellets proved successful. The tench were being caught simply with float fishing with sweetcorn. There is also a stretch of the River Tamar to try. Trout, grayling and salmon can be caught in their respective seasons.

Rules/Bans: No night fishing. No keepnets. Barbless hooks only.

Number of Lakes: One, plus a stretch of the River Tamar.

Facilities: Food outlet nearby. Sat Nav: PL15 9SP

Accommodation: Caravan Club Campsite. Cottages available for hire.

Telephone: 01566 776456 mob: 07708 994576

East Kitcham Farm

St. Giles on the Heath, near Launceston.

Ticket Price: Day permit costs £5 and night fishing is available by arrangement only.

Directions: From Launceston, head north east on the A388. Go through Dutson and turn right after around three miles, heading for Broadwoodwidger. After about a mile and a half look out for the signpost to the farm and fishery.

Description: Set within a working farm close to the Devon border, this small half acre pond is well worth a try. Stocked with hard fighting carp that are still in single figures but growing fast due to the abundance of natural food available. The tench and bream both come out on worm or sweetcorn. At one end of the pond the water is quite shallow, only two feet in areas. This area is well worth trying when it's a warm sunny day. A great simple little fishery but be prepared for a fair walk through the field to the waters edge.

Types of Fish:

Rules/Bans: Barbless hooks only. No keepnets. Fishing from dawn till dusk only.

Number of Lakes: One

Facilities: Food outlet nearby.

Accommodation: The farm offers self-catering accommodation. Fishing is free for those staying on site.

Telephone: 01566 784325   **Sat Nav:** PL15 9SL

East Rose Coarse Fishery

St Breward, Bodmin, Cornwall.

Ticket Price: Adults £6.00. Under 16's, disabled and OAP £4.00. Reduced prices for guests.

Directions: East Rose is located on Bodmin Moor above the ancient Delphy Bridge between the villages of Blisland and St. Breward.

Description: The fishery consists of four lakes, half a mile of pathways and numerous picnic areas to take in the wonderful natural scenery. The fishing lakes are perfect for the relaxed angler wanting peace and quiet away from the crowds, and are stocked with tench, bream, crucian carp, roach, rudd and carp ranging in size, up to 13lbs. There's a variety of lakes to suit all abilities, with small islands and reed beds to target.

Types of Fish:

Rules/Bans: Barbless hooks only. No keepnets. All fish must be returned quickly and carefully. Proof of an EA rod license is required.

Number of Lakes: Four

Facilities:

Accommodation: Seven excellent holiday cottages to hire.

Telephone: 01208 850674

Sat Nav: PL30 4NL

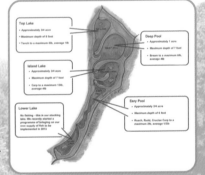

Ferndale fishing Lakes

Rockhead, Delabole.

SAT NAV PL33 9BU

Ticket Price: Adults Day £6 for 2 rods, £5 for 1 rod.
Under 14's/OAP's £5 for 2 rods, £4 for 1 rod.
Adults after 5 - 2 rods £5, after 5 - 1 rod £4.
Under 14's/OAP's after 5 - 1or 2 rods £4.

Directions: From Port Isaac take the B3267. At the T-junction turn left onto the B3314. Follow this road until you reach Delabole. Go through the village and look out for the fishery on your right, just before Rockhead.

Description: Ferndale Park has three well-stocked coarse fishing lakes located in a very relaxing and secluded valley.
Well stocked with mirror and common carp weighing into double figures. Rudd, roach, bream, tench and crucian carp are plentiful. The car park and toilet are adjacent to the lakes.
There are also ample picnicking areas around the lakes.
A great day out for any coarse angler beginner or experienced.

Types of Fish:

Number of Lakes: Three

Rules/Bans: Night fishing per person £10. You must be over 18 to night fish or if under 18 you must be supervised by an Adult. Barbless hooks only. No keepnets.

Facilities: ♿ 🚹 P **Telephone:** 01840 211017
Mob: 07790 246580

Fishery Location See page 9 **10**

Accommodation: None   **Sat Nav:** PL33 9BU

Glenleigh Fishery

Glenleigh Farm, Sticker, Nr St. Austell.

SAT NAV PL26 7JB

Ticket Price: Summer Day Ticket - £6.50. Winter Day ticket - £5.00. Tickets available on the bank. Open dawn until dusk.

Directions: From Truro take the A390 and come off at Hewas Water. Head towards Sticker and take your first left turn after about a mile. Follow this road back over the A 390, past Glenleigh Park. Look out for the farm and fishery on your left hand side.

Description: This beautiful one acre lake is set within a working farm that has holiday cottages for hire.
Stocked with an great assortment of fish including amongst others carp, tench, perch, roach, bream, rudd with some large specimen fish caught every year. It has very natural surroundings and well placed fishing platforms. The carp reach 25lbs and the impressive tench are 7lbs plus. Try fishing for the huge perch that reach 4lbs. There is a large car park with disabled access and disabled platforms to fish from.

Types of Fish:

Rules/Bans: Normal fishery rules apply and are available on the noticeboard at the entrance to the lake.

Number of Lakes: One   **Sat Nav:** PL26 7JB

Facilities: **Telephone:** 01726 73154

Accommodation: Luxury holiday cottages to hire.

Goonhavern Fishery

Oak Ridge Farm, Bodmin Road, Goonhavern, Newquay.

Ticket Price: Adults £5.00. Children/OAP's £4.00.

Directions: From Newquay take the A392 heading south. When you reach a roundabout turn right onto the A3075, signposted Goonhaven. When you reach Goonhaven turn left onto the B3285. After a mile you will see a sign for the fishery on your right.

Description: Goonhavern Fishery Lake is approximately 2 acres and is stocked with carp, tench, rudd, roach and perch. The fishery is open throughout the year and permits are available on the bank. There are plenty of lily beds and overhanging trees to target the good sized carp which I'm told reach 28lbs. If you like to catch specimen size perch this is the water to try, many are around 4lbs in weight. Try meat or corn for the smaller carp and tench. Float fish worm, caster or maggot for plenty of silver fish. The shallow end near the car park produces well in the warmer months.

Types of Fish:

Rules/Bans: Barbless hooks and no carp in keepnets. Fishing dawn till dusk only.

Number of Lakes: One

Sat Nav: TR4 9QG

Facilities:

Telephone: 01872 575052 - 07966 788994

Accommodation: Holiday cottages available, that sleep up to six people.

Muddy Puddles

Gwinear Farm
Near Cubert, Newquay.

Ticket Price: Gwinear Specimen Lake - Adults 1 Rod £7.00. 2 Rods £12.00. Juniors/ OAP 1 rod £5.00. 2 rods £12.00. Windsor Pools - Adults 1 Rod only £8.00. Juniors/ OAP £6.00

Directions: From Newquay take the A3075 heading south. After approximately five miles look out for the entrance to the farm on your right hand side.

Description: The four privately owned well stocked coarse fishing lakes have islands and varying water depths, with features including reeds, wildflowers and water lilies. Anglers of all levels of experience will enjoy catching the variety of fish including carp, bream, tench, perch, rudd and roach – all in abundance large and small. The Specimen Lake is one of the best specimen lakes in Cornwall, established in 1988 it has carp up to 34lbs. Day ticket payment is via a self service kiosk.

Types of Fish:

Number of Lakes: Four

Rules/Bans: See sign on site.

Facilities:

Sat Nav: TR8 5JX

Accommodation: Tranquil caravaning and camping with nice pitches, electric hookups and facilities available from £12 per day.

Telephone: 01637 830165   **Mobile:** 07802 400050

Hele Barton Coarse Fishery

Week St. Mary, Bude.

SAT
EX22 6XR
NAV

Ticket Price: Fishing is free for guests, and £5 per day (up to two rods) for non-guests.

Directions: From the M5 at Exeter, take the A30 route towards Cornwall. Turn off the A30 at Launceston and take the Bude road (B3254) for approximately 8 miles.
On entering Week St. Mary take the third left turn signposted Bude / Penhallam. Take a left turn signposted Week St. Mary. After leaving Week St. Mary take the first left turn for Poundstock / Penhallam. This takes you down a long steep hill. Take the 1st left turn signposted Jacobstow. The farm lane is about half a mile up the hill and is the first turning on the right.

Description: There are three lakes to fish at Hele Barton, and they are just minutes from the coast. The main lake at this superb fishery is about 1.5 acres and is well stocked with carp and tench to 12lbs. Come prepared to catch plenty of fish, mainly carp and tench but there are some silvers in these lakes. Hair-rigged meat or large pellets with a size 12 hook will get you the carp. Sweetcorn or bread will work for the tench. Don't forget the reed margins in the evening, great entertainment.

Types of Fish:

Rules/Bans: Barbless hooks only. No fixed rigs. No keepnets or carp sacks. No particle baits (nuts and pulses) except sweetcorn. No fires or radios. Under 14's must be accompanied by an adult at all times. All anglers must have a suitable landing net and disgorger.

Accommodation: 4 and 5 star accommodation is available in cottages that all have stunning views.

Facilities: **Telephone:** 01288 341622

Number of Lakes: Three   **Sat Nav:** EX22 6XR

23

Hengar Manor

Hengar Manor Country Park, St. Tudy, Bodmin.

SAT NAV PL30 3PL

Ticket Price: £7.50 per day purchased at reception / fishing shop or £12.50 if purchased at the lake. Please telephone for availability during peak holiday periods.

Directions: Turn off the A39 onto the B3266, follow signs to St. Tudy. Stay on the B3266 and you will see the park signposted.

Description: Hengar Manor is a superb venue for fishing holidays in Cornwall. The tranquil and well-stocked coarse fishing lakes are open all year and Stewart, the Lakes Manager, is there to help with your angling needs. The onsite bait & tackle shop provides guests with advice; you can also arrange fishing lessons, hire tackle and purchase all your tackle and bait. The four fishing lakes, range in size from a quarter to just over one and a half acres in size. They provide the perfect experience for the beginner, as well as offering more challenging conditions for the experienced angler who prefers to fish for larger specimens. The lakes are stocked with carp, tench, bream and roach. Manor Lake, the largest, has produced carp to 20lbs. Willow lake is over half an acre in size and has thirteen fishing platforms. It offers the angler fantastic silver fish fishing, along with plenty of carp.

Nature Lake is the smallest lake at Hengar at around a quarter of an acre in size. There are 8 pegs on this lake all fishing is from the natural bank. Pines Lake is the newest lake. It has 12 wooden fishing platforms and has recently been stocked with thousands of rapidly growing carp.

Types of Fish:

Rules/Bans: For more information on the lakes, including bait bans and rules, ask to speak to the bailiff at the fishing tackle shop.

Facilities: Tackle shop on-site.

Accommodation: Waterside cabins, holiday lodges, park bungalows, apartments and cottages are available for holiday lets.

Number of Lakes: 4

Telephone:
01208 850382

Houndapitt Farm Lake

Houndapitt Farm Cottages, Sandymouth Bay, Bude.

Ticket Price: Free fishing for all guests staying in cottages.

Directions: From the A39 "Atlantic Highway". Take the turning signposted to Sandymouth Bay and Stibb. Continue along this road until you have passed through the hamlet of Stibb. Follow the road signposted to Sandymouth Bay - Houndapitt Farm is on the right hand side and is signposted at the top of the lane.

Description: Great location with lovely views towards the sea. The ponds are stocked with various carp, golden tench, golden Rudd, common and mirror carp. Try fishing up to the small island or against the numerous reed bed margins. Plenty of silver fish, which will keep the children happy, can be caught on bread punch or maggot. Pellet or sweetcorn attract the carp and tench. This is an ideal holiday spot for families that like to do a bit of pleasure fishing.

Types of Fish:

Rules/Bans: Not many rules and bans, see details on-site.

Number of Lakes: Two

Accommodation: Nine cottages are available from 2 to 6 guests.

Facilities: P

Telephone: 01288 355 455

Sat Nav: EX23 9HW

16
Fishery Location
See page 9

25

2/11/17

Handwritten: ∂∂ ROACH RUDD PERCH

Langarth Pools

A390 between Truro and Chiverton.

SAT TR4 8QW NAV

Ticket Price: Day ticket £5. After 5pm £4. Weekly £20.
Junior/OAP: Day ticket £3. After 5pm £2. Weekly £15.

Directions: The fishery can be found on the A390 between Truro and Chiverton. Turn down the track that is virtually opposite Lanes Storage. Do not use the track marked Rosedean only but the track that passes next to the bungalow. Follow the track down the hill past some houses on the left hand side. At the bottom of the hill you will see the car park on your right.

Description: These two ponds are run very well by Threemilestone Angling Club. The larger General Lake has some small carp, tench, crucian carp, bream, roach and perch. If you want to catch carp up to 21lbs then fish the smaller Carp Lake furthest from the car park. Float fish for carp with pellet or sweetcorn but if that fails try leger hair-rigged boilies to the middle of the lake. On the General Lake keep it nice and simple and you will catch plenty of different species, many of them close to the bank.

Types of Fish:

Rules/Bans: No nuts.
Barbless hooks only.
No keepnets. Night fishing (members only) **Number of Lakes:** Two

Facilities: ♿ 🚻 🅿 Food outlets nearby.

17
Fishery Location
See page 9

Accommodation: Caravan and camp site nearby.

Telephone: 01872 272578 or 07734 445133   Sat Nav: TR4 8QW

Lostwithiel Hotel

Lostwithiel Golf & Country Club, Lower Polscoe, Lostwithiel.

Ticket Price: Members £4.00. Non members £5.00.
Senior Citizens and Juniors (under 16) £4.00.

Directions: From St. Austell take the A390 towards Lostwithiel. Follow the road through the town and take the first left after the railway line on to Cott Road. Follow the road until you reach the hotel.

Description: There are two well stocked lakes, set in attractive surroundings, at the centre of the golf course.
Fairway Lake is a two acre lake well stocked with common, mirror, and crucian carp, roach small to large, and good sized eels to 5lbs. Most fish will be 3 to 12lbs, but there are some unidentified large fish, estimated to be over 18lbs. These have been there for years, but never caught - yet! Swan Lake is a smaller lake and is stocked with crucian carp, roach and rudd. For carp try legering hair- rigged meat or corn. Surface fished crust, dog biscuits or pellets can be rewarding when its warm. The Crucians, while very sizable, are finicky. Try for them with float fished bread, corn or at any time maggot. Fish close in and use a delicate float set up. Roach and rudd sport can be had on float fished maggot or caster, over loose feed. Try for the big eels on legered large lobworms.

Types of Fish:

Rules/Bans: All catches must be returned to the water. Unhooking mats are compulsory. No keep nets, or fixed method feeders. Two rods only, barbless and micro barbed hooks only. No fixed leads, running leads only. Groundbait only in moderation. No peanuts / tiger nuts.

Facilities:

Number of Lakes: Two
Sat Nav: PL22 0HQ

Accommodation: In the hotel. **Telephone:** 01208 873550

Lower Lynstone Lakes

Trelowen, Lynstone Road, Bude.

SAT NAV EX23 0LR

Ticket Price: Daily Rates are £5.00 per person, with £3.50 (under 16) and £3.50 (60 and over on Monday to Friday)

Directions: From Bude, take the Widemouth Bay Road. About 1/2 a mile from the Crescent Post Office you will see a sign to the lakes on your left. Take the left turn opposite Upper Lynstone Caravan Park and the lakes will be found on the left after about 1/2 mile.

Description: There are two lakes in a tranquil setting adjacent to Bude Canal. A great but relatively new fishery with mirror and common carp up to around 16lbs, green tench and crucian and leather carp. Most tactics work for the carp but try small bits of luncheon meat on a size 16 hook close in. The tench prefer sweetcorn and tend to hold up in the middle of the ponds. If you want a fish a chuck the silver fish can be caught with a pint of maggots and a short pole. If you can't get to a tackle shop, punched bread works just as well.

Types of Fish:

Rules/Bans: Barbless hooks only.
No boilies. Ground bait - not advisable.
No keepnets. No fixed rigs. No radios. Under 14s must be accompanied by an adult. No fishing in the Canal.

Number of Lakes: Two   **Telephone:** 01288 352726

Facilities: ♿ 🚻 🅿️   **Sat Nav:** EX23 0LR

19
Fishery Location
See page 9

Accommodation: Self-catering accommodation at Trewhel-ju. Anglers staying in this accommodation get free fishing at Lower Lynstone lakes.

Mawgan Porth Pools-Lake

Retorrick Mill, Newquay.

SAT TR8 4BH NAV

Ticket Price: Day Tickets £7.00. Special Pensioners day on Thursdays £6.00. Season tickets cost £95.00. Pensioners season tickets cost £65.00.
Gates open at 7.30am - fishing until dusk.

Directions: Follow the A30 (Bodmin-Redruth) road, then take the A39 following the signs for the Airport and the brown coarse fishing signs on the (A3059). Just as you see the Airport, don't pass it, turn to your left, go down a steep hill into the village of St. Mawgan. Go up a steep hill, turn left, continue for two hundred yards then turn right at Sun Haven Valley Holiday Park, follow the lane down to the fishery.

Description: There are two lakes to chose from. Match Lake is 1.5 acres with depths that vary, but at a Maximum of approximately 3 metres. This lake is stocked with tench, bream, rudd & mainly carp, weighing up to 6lbs and averaging just under 3lbs. The smaller of the two lakes which has only 11 pegs is the Specimen Lake also called Horse Shoe Pool (because of the shape). It is stocked with carp, tench, bream, blue & golden orfe weighing up to 15lbs.

Types of Fish:

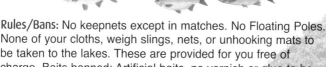

Rules/Bans: No keepnets except in matches. No Floating Poles. None of your cloths, weigh slings, nets, or unhooking mats to be taken to the lakes. These are provided for you free of charge. Baits banned: Artificial baits, no varnish or glue to be used on baits, all meats, tiger nuts, boilies and peanuts.

Facilities: Bait and tackle shop with tackle hire if required.

Accommodation: Caravan and camping on site. Electric hook up and showers.

Telephone: 01637 860770   **Number of Lakes:** Two

Meadowside Fisheries

The Cornish Birds of Prey Centre, Winnards Perch, St. Columb.

Ticket Price: Members Only - Adults £80 per year (2rods), £100 per year (3rods) Concessions £60 per year (2rods), £80 per year (3rods) Members can bring a guest for £10 per day.

SAT TR9 6DH NAV

Directions: Meadowside Fisheries is situated on the A39 at Winnards Perch, halfway between St. Columb Major and Wadebridge and approximately 12 miles from Newquay.

Description: There are 2 well stocked coarse fishing lakes set within the Cornish Birds of Prey Centre, located down in a valley both with islands and sheltered pegs. Middle Lake is a man-made lake two acres in size featuring four islands and depths from 5 feet to 10 feet. Its stocked with mirror and common carp to 20lbs, roach to 2lbs, perch to 3.5lbs, bream to 7lbs, tench to 5lbs plus skimmers. Bottom Lake covers one and a half acres, featuring one island and depths from 5 feet to 12 feet. Bottom Lake has carp to 15lbs, tench to 4lbs and still water barbel to 4lbs. Best tactics and baits include 14mm trout pellets on hair-rig for carp, swim feeder with corn or maggot for roach. Worm or double maggot for perch, Bread, corn or worm for bream and groundbait feeder with corn or worm for tench and barbel.

Types of Fish:

Rules/Bans: Barbless hooks only.
No keepnets [except in matches]
Unhooking mats must be used for carp. Fish straight ahead only.

Facilities:

Sat Nav: TR9 6DH

Telephone: 01637 880544   **Number of Lakes:** Two

21
Fishery Location
See page 9

Mellonwatts Mill

Pensagillas Park, Grampound, Truro.

Ticket Price: Prices start from £5.00 per day.

Directions: Turn right for Truro off the A390. Follow this road for approx 2-3 miles and fork left for the B3287 (the sign should say Tregony on it). Follow this road for 2 miles. At the end of the road is a T junction, turn left at this junction. Follow this road for 1 mile. You will see the sign for Pensagillas at the end of the drive.

Description: Mellonwatts Mill Lake is set in beautiful surroundings and is approx 2 acres in size. There is a very good selection of fish such as carp, roach, tench and golden rudd, which have now grown to a very nice size. The carp range from 1lb to 28lbs in weight and recently more mirror and common carp have been added to the existing stock. There are good car parking facilities and clean toilets. Refreshments can be supplied if pre-arranged. The lakes are only a few hundred yards away from the campsite so you can combine your passion for fishing with your holiday.

Types of Fish:

Number of Lakes: One   **Sat Nav:** TR2 4SR

Facilities:

Accommodation: Electric hook-up for caravans. Tents available for rent.

Telephone: Phone: 01872 530808   Mobile: 07967827340

Mid Cornwall fisheries

Summercourt, just off the A30.

Ticket Price: Yearly Membership for Carp Lake £250.00. Match Lake Day Ticket £6.00. Book on-line or phone before setting off.

Directions: Located at Guanabaras which is just off the A30, right in the middle of Cornwall, hence the name Mid Cornwall Fisheries. It is located in a peaceful wooded valley, situated approximately 2 miles past the Clock Garage, Summercourt. When you book to fish you will be provided with further directions and the combination number for the gate.

Description: The Carp Lake (specimen lake) is around 3 acres in size and is stocked with nearly eighty double figure carp, half of which are above 20lbs. The majority of the fish in this lake are the fast growing simmo strain and are growing all the time. This lake can only be fished via yearly membership and promises a tranquil and relaxing fishing environment.
The 24 peg Match Lake is now open for weekend matches or day tickets. It has been been stocked with immaculate carp of up to 4lbs in weight and also includes some large tench. This lake is highly stocked ensuring excellent bags for the match angler and pleasure angler alike. Guanabaras Match Lake, also known as Neils Lake has a huge stock of silver fish, some tench and a number of very large perch.

Types of Fish:

Number of Lakes: Three

Accommodation: Carp Lodge available for weekly hire.

Facilities: ♿ 🚻 🅿️

Telephone: 07779 285550

23
Fishery Location
see page 9

Rules/Bans: No tiger nuts, peanuts or animal feed. Only pellets, hemp and particles purchased from the fishery can be used. Bait boats are allowed. For more fishery rules see on site list.

Middle Boswin fishery

Middle Boswin Farm, Wendron, Helston.

SAT
TR13 0HR
NAV

Ticket Price: Coarse Lake: £5:00 - Adult day ticket.
£4:00 - Concession.
Trout Lake: £17:50 - 2 fish adult ticket.
£15:00 - Concession. £14:00 - catch and release.
Open 7am-9pm (winter dawn until dusk)

Directions: From A394 Falmouth, turn right beside Rame Post
Office. Then left at the T-junction. Drive through Carnkie and
Porkellis. At the Star Inn T-junction turn right. Take the first right
at Riversleigh Cottage. The fishery is the third on the left.

Description: The one acre coarse lake is an ideal venue for the
pleasure angler, as well as being a great bagging water for the
more experienced angler. Stocked with a variety of fish you
should catch all day. The lake is stocked with carp to 10lb, chub
to 6lb and roach reaching 2lb plus. Crucian carp, rudd, perch
and skimmers will also show to most baits, so be prepared for a
good mixed bag. It has an island in the middle and some small
patches of lilies. Float fishing with corn, worm, maggot/caster or
carp pellet are proven to be the best method. Don't ignore the
margins. Some of the best fish have been caught less than a
rod length out. The trout lake is well stocked with rainbow trout
plus a good head of brown and some blues.

Types of Fish:

Rules/Bans: Barbless hooks only (micro/whisker barb included)
No fixed ledgers. No keep nets or sacks (except in matches)
Baited rods must not be left unattended, max 2 rods per person.
No hemp, tiger nuts, peanuts or catfood.

Facilities: ♿ 🚻 P ☕ Tackle
shop on-site.

24
Fishery Location
See page 9

Telephone: 01209 860420   **Accommodation:** Cottages near by.

Number of Lakes: One coarse lake, one trout lake.

Nance Lakes

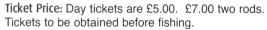

Trevarrack Lelant, St. Ives.

SAT TR26 3EZ NAV

Ticket Price: Day tickets are £5.00. £7.00 two rods. Tickets to be obtained before fishing.

Directions: Take the B3306 from St. Ives. Turn left onto the B3311 towards Penzance. Turn left again towards Trevarrack / Lelant Downs. The fishery is signed on your left.

Description: The three privately owned stocked fishing lakes have islands and varying water depths, with features including reeds, wildflowers and water lilies. Anglers of all levels of experience will enjoy catching the variety of fish including bream, carp, roach, tench and more – all in abundance large and small. The swims are a good size, everyone is friendly and the views are great.
I've only fished the first small lake close to the car park but its a great location and quiet as well. Good size swims and never seems to get too busy.

Types of Fish:

Rules/Bans: All visitors must check in at the front desk before looking/fishing. Any visitor caught littering will be asked to leave and there are no tins or glass containers allowed on site. Any fish caught must be landed with a landing net and unhooked in the landing net. (Carp mats are advised) Barbless hooks only. (Biggest hook is size 10) Baited rods must not be left unattended.

Number of Lakes: Three

Facilities: 🅿 🏕 🚐 ♿ 🚻 Food outlet nearby.

Accommodation: Nance Lakes welcomes Caravans of all shapes and sizes with our generously sized levelled pitches, all of which are right next to our superb facilities including luxurious toilets with walk in hot water shower blocks.

25 Fishery Location See page 9

Telephone: 01736 740348   **Sat Nav:** TR26 3EZ

Oakside Fishery

NO PERCH ?

Oakside Lodge, Whitecross, Newquay.

Ticket Price: Adults up to 2 rods £6.00. Concessions £5.00.
Night tickets...(dusk till dawn) £6.00. Concessions £5.00.
24 hour tickets £10.00. Concessions £9.00.

Directions: From the edge of Newquay take the A392. When you reach Quintrell Downs turn right at the roundabout onto the A3058. Continue on this road and turn left after Dairyland Farm World and follow the lane to the fishery.

Description: This is an excellent carp fishing venue, well stocked with both young carp and mature wiley individuals reaching up to the 30lb mark. With well spaced maintained swims, islands to target, secluded lily covered coves, overhanging trees and mature reed beds, you will love the feel of this lake. The lake is also an exciting match/coarse fishing venue with hosts of bream, crucian, tench, roach, rudd and skimmers in abundance. Oakside has good access with even parking available close to some of the swims for the not so mobile angler.

Types of Fish:

Rules/Bans: No tiger nuts or peanuts. No carp in keep nets. Barbless hooks only. Use common sense.

Number of Lakes: One

Facilities:

Sat Nav: TR8 4QL

Telephone:
0777 3224243 (Brian)
07970125840 (Sandra)
0798 0808506 (Darren)

Penvose Farm Fishery

Penvose Farm Holidays, St. Mawgan, Near Newquay

SAT NAV: TR8 4AE

Ticket Price: Fishing is free to Penvose static caravan residents. Reduced fee to camping and touring residents. Day tickets are also available to non-residents dawn to dusk (Night fishing is only available to Penvose residents)

Directions: From Newquay take the B3276 North towards Padstow. At Watergate keep on the B3276 heading inland towards the Airport, as you leave Tregurrian. The fishery is the next right turn before the sharp left bend.

Description: Three mature stream fed lakes nestling in a delightful Cornish valley are only a short walk from the holiday accommodation available. All lakes feature double figured carp, rudd, roach, bream, perch and tench. The main attraction at the lakes are the carp which grow up to 28lbs. The most effective means of catching them is using poled corn or pellet. Surface fishing works well on warm days. Don't forget the reed margins in the evenings.

Types of Fish: Common Carp 15-16lb, Mirror Carp 16-17lb, Ghost Carp 19.5-20lb. Green Tench 3-4lb, Golden Tench 8oz, Bream 4-5lb. Crucians 1.5lb, Rudd 1.5lb, Roach 1lb.

Number of Lakes: Three

Facilities: ♿ 🚻 🅿 🏕 🚐   Sat Nav: TR8 4AE

27 Fishery Location see page 9

Accommodation: 2 & 3 Bedroom Holiday Caravans.

Telephone: 01637 860277 or 01637 860432 Mob: 07811 531881

Perran Springs

Perran Springs Holiday Park, Goonhavern, Truro.

Ticket Price: One week permits are available for people staying on site only. Person aged 12 and over – first rod £22.00. Each extra rod £15.00. (maximum 3 rods per person)

Directions: Travelling westwards through Cornwall, by-pass the village of Indian Queens, remaining on the A30. Continue straight over the roundabout by the wind turbines, signed 'Redruth A30' and 'Perranporth B3285'. After 1.5 miles turn right at the Boxheater junction, onto the B3285 signed 'Perranporth' and 'Goonhavern'. Continue along the B3285 for 1.5 miles. The park entrance will then be clearly seen on the right hand side.

Description: Mayfly Lake holds a variety of species including 20lb. plus carp, big tench and large bream. Fishing near the margins is best, either with a pole or rod, using a ledger or float. Butterfly Lake is great for family fishing, with carp up to 15lbs, tench, big perch, rudd, roach and bream. Best method is with a pole by the islands. Total catches of 50lb plus are not uncommon. Dragonfly Lake is recommended for the more experienced and patient carp angler. The majority of carp in this lake are between 10 to 20lbs.

Types of Fish:

Rules/Bans: Barbless hooks only.
No keepnets. See other rules on-site.

Number of Lakes: Three

Facilities: Tackle shop on-site.

Accommodation: Caravan holiday homes.

Telephone: 01872 540568   **Sat Nav:** TR4 9QG

Porth Reservoir

SAT NAV TR8 4JS

Near Newquay.

Ticket Price: Day tickets £6.50 for adults. £5.00 concessions. Tickets must be purchased from the self-service machine before fishing.

Directions: From Newquay take the A3059 towards St. Columb Major. Go past Porth and turn right after the golf course. Porth Reservoir is signposted on your left, opposite RAF St. Mawgan.

Description: A picturesque and peaceful site which is run by South West Lakes Trust. This mature 40 acre water produces great sport with weights of 130lbs plus caught by pleasure anglers. Bream to 10lbs, good tench, rudd to 2lbs, roach 2lbs plus, carp to 32lbs and pike to 24lbs.
Try a groundbait feeder fishing with worm or pellet on the hook for the bream. Ledger for the carp with hair rigged meat or boillies. This is also a great winter venue for the pike which reach 25lbs.

Types of Fish: Carp, Bream, Rudd, Roach, Tench, Pike, Perch and Eels.

Rules/Bans: Barbless hooks only.   **Number of Lakes:** One

Facilities: Food outlets nearby.

Accommodation: Trebarber Farm Holidays nearby.

29
Fishery Location See page 9

Telephone: 01209 860301   **Sat Nav:** TR8 4JS (nearby)

38

Prince Park

St Wenn, Nr Bodmin.

SAT PL30 5PD NAV

Ticket Price: Adult day tickets £6.00.
Registered disabled, OAPs and under 16s £5.00.
Pay at the house on the way in.

Directions: Head towards Truro on the A30 and come off at the Victoria Interchange. Take the last exit on the roundabout signposted Withiel. At the next roundabout turn left and immediately left again. Take the next right and turn left at the crossroads. Head towards St. Wenn, the fishery is well signposted on your right.

Description: This lovely looking peaceful half acre pond has a small island in the middle with plenty of lily beds. The island is the perfect spot to target the carp which reach 15lbs. Most of the margins have reed beds that also attract the carp especially in the warm summer evenings. Bream reach 5lbs and there are some huge crucian carp over 3lbs! Punched bread or soft hookable pellets for the crucian. Avoid maggot or caster unless you want to catch a lot of small roach.

Types of Fish:

Rules/Bans: No Keepnets. Barbless hooks only.
Unhooking mats and large landing nets are advised.
Closed from 1st. November until Easter.

Number of Lakes: One

Facilities: Food outlets nearby.

30

Accommodation: Nearby.

Telephone: 01726 890095   **Sat Nav:** PL30 5PD

Snowland Fisheries

Snowland Leisure, Par Farm, Par.

SAT PL24 2AE NAV

Ticket Price: Day tickets are available from the lake, reception and cafe at a cost of 5.00 per angler per day. Under 16s / OAPs / Disabled £3.00.

Directions: M5-A38-A390 via Plymouth and Liskeard. Go over the Tamar Bridge on the A38 go past Liskeard to Dobwalls. At the roundabout in Dobwall turn 2nd. left signposted A390 St. Austell and go via Lostwithiel to St. Blazey. At St. Blazey go over the railway crossing, past the petrol station, approx 1/4 mile to the traffic lights.
Turn left at the lights (signposted to Par) via Station Rd. Carry straight on past the bus depot to the mini roundabout and turn left into Harbor Rd, then turn left again (sign-posted Fowey). Snowland fisheries is now first left.

Description: There are currently two pools available with a third in the process of being completed. The main lake has recently been reopened after a period of some 15 years. There are 27 pegs and all have solid platforms. Pegs 1 - 5 have parking close by and there is one peg totally dedicated for wheelchair access, although all pegs on the roadside are suitable for disabled access. The lakes contain tench, perch, mirror carp, common carp, rudd, roach, bream, crucian carp and a few brown trout.

Types of Fish:

Rules/Bans: The use of the following are strictly prohibited: Boilies, Braid, Cat meat, Keepnets (except in matches)

31 Fishery Location See page 9

Facilities: Bait and tackle shop on-site

Accommodation: Lakeside caravans available for holidays.

Telephone: 01726 825058 / 07598 392278   **Lakes: Three**

St. Tinney Farm

St. Tinney Farm Fishing Holidays, Otterham.

Ticket Price: £15, per rod, per person, per week.

Directions: From Bude take the A39 signposted Wadebridge, drive through the village of Wainhouse Corner. After 11 miles from Bude there is a short stretch of uphill dual carriageway, when you reach the brow of the hill you will see a sign for Otterham village. Turn left, then follow the road to your right, then take the first turning on your right, following the road around through Churchtown Farm, following the brown signs to St. Tinney Farm.

Description: The fishery at St.Tinney has been designed to accommodate a variety of skill levels, from beginners to life long anglers, with different lake types and species of fish. Kingfisher Lake is a carp lake and a must for any angler. The average weight per fish is 5lbs. There are comfortable pegs to fish from and a host of features. Moorhen Lake is entirely devoted to Silver fish, with high number's of skimmer bream, roach and rudd. It is a great lake for anglers who wish to try catching something other than carp, or a beginner wetting their first line. Mallard Lake is a specimen carp lake, stocked with 50 hand picked carp.

Types of Fish: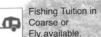

Rules/Bans: See full list on-site.   **Number of Lakes:** Five

Facilities: Fishing Tuition in Coarse or Fly available.

Accommodation: Lodges, cottages and caravans are are available for holiday hire.

Telephone: 01840 261274   Sat Nav: PL32 9TA

Pass Next

Trebellan Park

Cubert, Nr Newquay.

Ticket Price: Day tickets are £6 for 1 rod and £10 for 2 rods per person per day for all 12 years and above (under 12's are free).

Directions: Take the A3075 Perranporth Road from Newquay. After three miles turn right towards Cubert at the crossroads. After half a mile, take the first left and follow the signs to the fishery, located opposite the Smugglers Den Inn.

Description: Set in the Rejarrah Valley, Trebellan Park holiday park offers coarse fishing on three lakes. All the lakes average around 6ft. deep and all are stocked with similar species of fish. The carp go up to just under 30lbs, tench to around 4lbs and plenty of roach and rudd to 2lbs.

Legering is the best bet for carp using either hair rigged boilies, meat or corn. Tench love float fished corn, bread or worm whilst light tactics using maggots are ideal for the roach and rudd. This is also a great winter roach venue. The specimen lake is about 3 acres and is at the bottom of the valley, so no mobile phone signal! Make sure you have powerful gear for this lake as the carp are large and fight very hard.

Types of Fish:

Rules/Bans: Fishing dawn - dusk only. Barbless hooks only. No keepnets.

Facilities:

Accommodation: Two comfortable lodges and superbly converted Mill House apartments.

Number of Lakes: Three

Telephone: 01637 830522   **Sat Nav:** TR8 5PY

Trevella Park

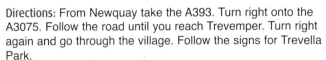

Trevella Holiday Park, Crantock, Newquay.

SAT NAV TR8 5EW

Ticket Price: Free – for park guests only.

Directions: From Newquay take the A393. Turn right onto the A3075. Follow the road until you reach Trevemper. Turn right again and go through the village. Follow the signs for Trevella Park.

Description: Trevella Lake is the more mature of the two lakes, and is an ideal water for all anglers. Covering approximately 3 acres there are plenty of swims to choose from. The water depth ranges from a few inches to about 16 feet, with the deepest part being at the far side of the main island as you look from the entrance. The lake has an abundance of carp, tench, bream, roach and rudd. Varieties of carp include, mirror, common, linear and ghost, as well as a good head of Crucian Carp. The lake record is standing at 27lb. 12oz.

Over the last 19 years Springfield Lake has matured into a fine specimen lake. There is now 150 good size carp, including some that are 24lb. plus and many in their late teens.

Types of Fish:

Rules/Bans: General fishing rules can be found on-site.

Number of Lakes: Two

Facilities:

34
Fishery Location
see page 9

Accommodation: Static caravans, holiday homes available. Dog friendly accommodation also available.

Telephone: 01637 830308

Sat Nav: TR8 5EW

Trewandra Coarse Fishing Lake

Trewandra Farm, Landrake, Saltash, close to Plymouth.

Ticket Price: Adults £6.00. Children £3.00.
(under 13yrs. must be supervised at all times)
After 4pm until dusk. Adults £4.00. Children £2.00.
Night fishing available by arrangement only.

SAT NAV PL12 5JA

Directions: Trewandra coarse fishing lake is situated just 6 miles from Saltash. Take the A38 to Landrake, then the road to Blunts. After passing Dolbeare Caravan Park take the 2nd left and follow the fishing lake signs as far as the 1st. right. Then turn into the driveway and continue down to the car-park beside the lake.

Description: Trewandra Lake was formed from marsh land in 1995, designed for anglers and in a peaceful and secluded place, surrounded by 1 acre of lawns and ornamental trees. Anglers have enjoyed the sport of catching carp up to 18lbs, 2½ - 3lb tench, 1 - 2lb roach & skimmers and a few specimen larger bream. Anglers can drive to the car-park beside the lake.

Types of Fish:

Rules/Bans: See details on-site.

Number of Lakes: One

Facilities: A toilet is available from April to the end of September.

Accommodation: Caravan and camp site near by.

Telephone: 01752 851258   **Sat Nav:** PL12 5JA

35 Fishing Location See page 9

White Acres

White Acres Holiday Park, White Cross, Nr Newquay.

Ticket Price: Fishing is available for park guests only.

Directions: Follow the M4/M5 to Exeter then the A30 past Okehampton and Bodmin. From the A30 turn onto the A392 to Newquay, and travel over 1st roundabout. You will see the entrance to White Acres shortly after the roundabout on the right hand side.

Description: White Acres Holiday Park has become the ultimate resort for anglers and their families. Enjoy 10 pleasure lakes and 3 specimen lakes set in 184 acres of stunning Cornish countryside. The coarse fishing lakes provide the tranquillity and choice that will thrill anglers of all ages and abilities. There is something for every fisherman whether you are a pleasure, match or specimen angler. There are over 300 pegs, including wheelchair pegs, spread across the well stocked lakes. There is also an on park tackle shop as well as weekly resident matches and expert advice and tuition. With waters of various sizes and depths, you can fish for roach, tench, bream, F1's, catfish, rudd, perch, carp, barbel and chub.

Types of Fish:

Rules/Bans: See details on-site.   **Telephone:** 01726 862100

Accommodation: Caravan and Lodge holiday homes available.

Facilities:    Number of Lakes: 13
Sat Nav: TR8 4LW

Woodlay Fishing Holidays

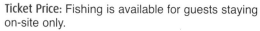

Woodlay Holidays, Herodsfoot, Liskeard.

Ticket Price: Fishing is available for guests staying on-site only.

Directions: From the M5 take the A38 to Plymouth. Continue on the A38 around Plymouth and over the Tamar Bridge. Continue on the A38 bypassing Liskeard (ignore all signs to Looe). At the new Dobwalls roundabout turn left onto the A390 towards St. Austell. After 2 miles at East Taphouse turn left onto the B3359 towards Looe (shortly after a garage on your right). Woodlay is on the left hand side after 3 miles, immediately before some large conifers.

Description: There are 6 fishing lakes of different sizes set in beautiful, peaceful woodland. The three larger lakes contain the large carp, the majority being double figures with a few over 20lbs. These lakes also have roach, rudd, tench, bream and perch . The fish caught are wonderfully fit and beautifully coloured. The smaller lakes contain tench, roach rudd, double figure carp and many smaller carp.

Types of Fish:

Rules/Bans: No keepnets to be used. Barbless hooks only.
Use of an unhooking mat is mandatory by all anglers. No sweetcorn. No nuts.

Facilities: ♿ 🚹 P

Number of Lakes: Six

Sat Nav: PL14 4RB

Accommodation: Eight apartments of various sizes available for holidays. **Telephone:** 01503 220221

Woonsmith Lagoon

Woonsmith Farm, Nancledra, Penzance.

SAT NAV TR20 8LP

Ticket Price: Adult day ticket (over 16) - £5.00.
Child day ticket (under 16) - £3.00.
Weekly Tickets - Adult full week day ticket - £20.00.
Child full week day ticket - £15.00.
Senior Citizen full week day ticket - £17.50.

Directions: From Penzance take the B3311. Take the 3rd. right onto Green Lane Hill / B3311. Turn left onto Trevarrack Rd. Turn right still on the B3311. Take the your first left. After one mile turn right to the lagoon.

Description: Consisting of a 1.5 acre lake which has 21 pegs. It is set in the beautiful Cornish countryside and well maintained privately. Woonsmith is stocked with well conditioned fish including specimen carp, tench, bream, perch, roach and rudd. Woonsmith is suitable for disabled persons with purpose built platforms and ramps leading down to the Lagoon.
Whether you are looking for a days fishing or a full season's fishing, Woonsmith Lagoon is the place to be. With its stunning views and fantastic location it really is hard to find a better place to fish.

Types of Fish:

Number of Lakes: One

Rules/Bans: All Hooks must be barbless.
Keepnets are allowed but with the following sub rules: No carp in keepnets at all. No fish over 3lbs. All nets must be dipped in the disinfectant tank prior to use. No night fishing. Groundbait is allowed but only in small amounts. No Tiger Nuts.

Facilities: ♿ 🚻 🅿️   Telephone: 01736 796925
Sat Nav: TR20 8LP

38
Fishery Location
See page 9

Yeomadon Farm

Border of Cornwall & Devon, Pyworthy, Holsworthy.

SAT NAV EX22 6SH

Ticket Price: Day Tickets £5.00. Concessions £4.00

Directions: From the A3072 follow signs to Holsworthy. Drive through the town centre and make a right turn to Waitrose Supermarket. Proceed straight across the mini-roundabout to the end of this road. Turn left to North Tamerton. Continue on this road for approx. 2 miles. You will see a white house (Brooks House) on the right, drive past the house and take the next right to Whitstone. Proceed along this road for approx. 1 mile; you will drive past East Yeomadon and Little Yeomadon. You will see the Yeomadon sign on a stone wall on the left.

Description: Four coarse fishing lakes set in peaceful farmland and woods. There are carp up to 20lbs and small tench, roach, bream and crucian carp. The lakes have always been mainly used by people staying at the cottages so they do not get over fished and the fish remain in good condition. The lakes are accessed by a network of gravel paths so that they are easily accessible. Park Lake has smaller fish in it which has proved popular with children as they can catch something fairly quickly. Woodpecker Lake is a 1 acre lake stocked with 40 carp from 12 - 20lbs. Kingcroft Lake is a 1/2 acre lake with carp from 6 - 15lbs and Tench to 3lbs. Smayhay Lake is another 1/2 acre lake with carp up to 14lbs.

Types of Fish:

Rules/Bans: All mats and nets must be disinfected before use. Barbless hooks only. No keepnets. Boilies and groundbait in moderation. No peanuts or particle bait.

Facilities: ♿ 🚻 🅿️   **Number of Lakes:** Four
Telephone: 01409 253378

39 Fishery Location See page 5

Accommodation: Four self-catering cottages sleeping up to 8.

South West Lakes Trust

South West Lakes Trust can offer something for every angler. There lakes range in size from 2-81 acres and are situated in areas of outstanding beauty and tranquility.

If you are looking for specimen carp up to 40lb+, pike to 30lb, bream to 15lb, Perch to 5lb or great match fishing with 100lb+ weights then look no further than the lakes of the South West.

The sites have toilet facilities, excellent disabled access with wheelchair platforms at some locations and ample car parking. Here are some of the fisheries run by South West Lakes Trust in Cornwall.

Argal Reservoir is a well established coarse fishery stocked with numerous big carp and pike over 30lb, bream over 15lb, roach and rudd. The lake record carp is 42lb 8oz and the water has been re-stocked during 2009 with a good number of carp. The site also has public lavatories including provision for disabled visitors, a children's play area and picnic tables.
Species: Carp, Pike, Tench, Bream, Roach, Rudd, Perch, Eels
Fishing Times: Open all year, 24 hours a day.
Day Permits: Day permit self-service units are available on site
Adult £6.50. Concession £5.00

Bussow fishery is conveniently placed for holiday anglers close to St.Ives and Penzance. Bussow has mirror and common carp to 28lb and was re-stocked with 50 carp weighing 4-5lb. Mixed bags of 30-40lb can be expected made up of rudd to 1½ lb, roach and good bream.
Species: Carp, Bream Rudd, Roach, Tench, Perch, Crucian Carp, Eels
Fishing Times: Open all year, 24 hours a day.
Day Permits: Adult £6.50. Concession £5.00.

Boscathnoe near Penzance is a mature 4 acre water for pleasure fishing with large lily beds and overhanging trees. Carp to 25lb, good bream and tench make for exciting sport.
Species: Carp, Tench, Bream, Roach, Rudd, Crucian carp, Eels
Fishing Times: Open all year, 24 hours a day.
Day Permits: Adult £6.50. Concession £5.00.

Upper Tamar Lake at Bude is a quiet lake, very well stocked with carp well over 30lb with a good head of 20's. The lake record is a 46lb mirror carp caught in 2007. 50lb+ bags of bream and roach can be expected to feeder, pole or waggler. Whip fishing is also very productive with bags up to 30lb of roach and rudd.
Species: Carp, Bream, Rudd, Roach, Perch, Eels.
Fishing Times: Open all year, 24 hours a day.
Day Permits: Adult £6.50. Concession £5.00.

SWLT Head Office (01566 771930)

Cornish River Fishing

In the north brown trout, grayling, and the occasional dace can be taken by fly on the Upper Tamar between Kingford Mill and Bridgerule.

Salmon, sea trout and brown trout on the Rivers Tamar, Ottery, Inny and Carey. Permits from The Fishing Department, Homeleigh Garden Centre, Dutson, Launceston.

Bodmin is the centre for salmon, sea trout and brown trout on the River Camel.

The River Fowey, 2 miles at Lanhydrock, for salmon and sea trout from 1st. April to 30th. Sept.

Salmon, sea trout and brown trout from the East and West Looe Rivers (also Rivers Fowey, Lynher, Inny, Seaton and Camel) from 1st. April to 15th. Dec.

Salmon, sea trout and brown trout on the River Fowey from 1st. April to 15th December.

Salmon, sea trout and brown trout on the River Inny, near Launceston from 1st. March to 14th. October. Early and late are the best times in the season for salmon with sea trout in the middle months.

River Fishing (tidal)

The River Fowey offers some excellent marks including the Blockhouse at the mouth of the river on the Polruan side.

The River Tamar offers numerous productive marks including: Toproint, Wilcove, Saltash quay & pontoon, Landulph, Halton Quay, Cotehele Quay.

Westcountry Angling Passport

The Token Scheme - how it works?

The scheme is a sheer delight for the roving angler as it is operated through a unique token payment system. This allows anglers to access any of the participating fisheries when they want and without the need to contact anyone beforehand.

There is a vast choice of fishing on offer through the scheme; from the rushing moorland streams with wily, pocket-sized brown trout to the languid, meandering lowland streams with good mayfly hatches and their large brown trout; short spate rivers containing good runs of peal and the secluded farm lakes with their trout, carp and tench.

Token prices

Westcountry Angling Passport tokens cost £2.50 each and are supplied in books of 5 or 10 (£12.50 or £25.00). The tokens are valid for any beat but can only be used once. Beats are rated according to their quality, ease of fishing and species of fish and cost between 2 and 5 tokens. Tokens expire on 31st. December each year, and please note they cannot give refunds for unused tokens or exchange for the following year.

Five steps to get you fishing...

1) Using the website, or your Token Fishery Guide select which beat you would like to fish and, using the directions in your Guide, travel to the beat parking area.

2) The tokens come in three parts – before you start fishing – fill in the right hand part of the token and post the required number of tokens in the token box at the beat. The locations of the token boxes are detailed on the maps provided.

3) Get fishing....tight lines!

4) When you have finished fishing - complete a catch return - fill in the middle part of the token with catch details (and any other comments) and post in the token box at the beat.

5) The last part of the token is for your records.

It is a requirement of using the Passport scheme that you submit a catch return and post it in the token box as this data is essential for monitoring the health of these rivers and provides useful information for other anglers. The fishery owners and Trust staff carry out checks to ensure your fishing is not disturbed by others abusing the scheme.

Telephone: 01579 372140

www.westcountryangling.com

Berrio Mill

River Lynher, Golberdon, Callington.

SAT
PL17 7NL
NAV

Ticket Price: Fishing is included for our holiday guests otherwise 3 tokens from Westcountry Angling Passport, the excellent fishing scheme operated by the Westcountry Rivers Trust. Visit www.westcountryangling.com for details and prices.

Directions: From Liskeard head north on Greenbank Rd / B3254 toward Greenbank Rd / B3254. Go through 2 roundabouts. At the next roundabout, take the 1st exit onto St. Cleer Rd / B3254. Continue to follow B3254. Continue straight onto Higher Rd. Continue onto Princess Rd. Continue onto Globerdon Rd. Turn left and you will see berrio Mill on your left.

Description: Enjoy some excellent river fishing for Sea Trout, Brown Trout and Salmon on the beautiful banks of the River Lynher at Berrio Mill. Trout can be fished from 16th March to 30th September and Salmon from the 1st March to 14th October. Large spring sea trout, spring salmon and late summer grilse. Trouting is good in May and June with peal from July. The Lynher is characterised by predominantly riffle/run sections and pocket water with occasional deep pools, however this compact section has 5 good holding pools! Fenced and cut out every winter, this beat has the possibility of producing some very good sea trout and salmon given adequate water. Fish with a shorter fly rod or worm/lure. If you only have a 9' or 10' fly rod, try filling a spare spool with some 10lb monofil and work a worm or two with a few split shot through the pools, runs and along the undercut banks. Locals get some brilliant results with these tactics. Fishing tuition and guidance is available.

Accommodation: Two holiday cottages available.

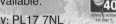
40
Fishing Location
See page 9

Telephone: 01579 363252   Sat Nav: PL17 7NL

Rivermead Farm

River Fowey, Twowatersfoot, Liskeard.

Ticket Price: River Fowey Fishing: Residents - Free of Charge
Non Residents £20.00 per day.
Brown Trout Lake: £30.00 two fish ticket, catch & keep only,
strictly fly fishing only.

Directions: From Liskeard take the A38. After approximately 6
miles you will come to the Halfway House Inn on your right.
Take the first turning on the right after the inn, signposted
'Mount, Warleggan & Cardinham'. Cross the river bridge and
you will find Rivermead Farm after 1/2 mile on the left.

Description: Rivermead Farm is nestled in 17 acres and located
just off the A38 between Liskeard and Bodmin offering some of
the most spectacular scenery with prime Salmon and Sea Trout
fishing on its own private half mile stretch of the River Fowey.
In order to give maximum enjoyment only 3 anglers are allowed
on the river at any one time. The season runs 1st. April to 15th.
December.
Trout fishing is also available on a 2 acre lake with various areas
that are open and shallow.
Tuition can be arranged by Rivermead Farm Cottages with a
local Ghillie but, in order to avoid disappointment, you must book
in advance. New skills and techniques can be taught whether
you are a beginner or a more advanced angler.

Accommodation: Five self-catering properties: four cosy
apartments within the barn and one detached period cottage.
They sleep 2 to 8 guests individually or a total of 20 if all
properties are combined

Number of Lakes: 1/2 mile stretch of River Fowey
plus one lake.

Telephone: 01208 821464   **Sat Nav:** PL14 6HT

F I S H I N G   T A C K L E
S H O P S
in Cornwall

Anglers Den, Hayle, Cornwall. Tel: 07733 272524

Atlantic Fishing Tackle, 9B Cliff Rd, Newquay, Cornwall. Tel: 01637 850777

Camel Valley Sportfishing, 5 Polmorla Rd, Wadebridge, Cornwall. l Tel: 01208 816403

City Angling Centre, Pydar, St Truro, Cornwall. Tel: 01872 275340

County Angler, 39 Cross St, Camborne, Cornwall. Tel: 01209 718490

Fairwater Fishing, Unit 3 Fish Quay, The Quay, Looe, PL13 1DX, Cornwall. Tel: 01503 269259

Fishing Mayhem, Plymouth Rd, Liskeard, Cornwall. Tel: 01579 340447

Jack Bray & Son, The Quay, East Looe, Looe, Cornwall. Tel: 01503 262504

Jim's Discount Tackle, 56 Fore St, Redruth, Cornwall. Tel: 01209 211903

Jim's Discount Tackle, 59 Causewayhead, Penzance, Cornwall. Tel: 01736 360160

Jim's Discount Tackle, 101 Trelowarren Street, Camborn, TR14 8AW. Tel: 01209 712758

JM Bray, Fore Street, East Looe, Cornwall, PL13 1AE. Tel: 01503 262677

Last Stop Tackle Shop, Haelarcher Farm Courtyard, The Lizard, TR127PF. T el: 07794 666781

LineBite Angling Centre, 10a, Eastcliffe Rd, St. Austell, Par, PL24 2AH. Tel: 01726 825103

Lowen-Chy Angling, 63, Clifden Rd, St. Austell, PL25 4PB, Cornwall. Tel: 01726 75631

Lure Heaven, 3, Newport Industrial Estate, Launceston, PL15 8EX, Cornwall. Tel: 01566 770822

Mermaid Fishing Tackle, The Old Smithy, Ross Bridge, Penzance, Cornwall. Tel: 07901 731201

Mevagissey Angling Centre, West Wharf, Mevagissey, Cornwall. Tel: 01726 843430

Newtown Angling Centre, Newtown, Germoe, Penzance, Cornwall. Tel: 01736 763721

Padstow Angling Centre, South Quay, Padstow, Cornwall. Tel: 01841 532762

Porthleven Angling Centre, Harbour Head, Helston, TR13 9JY, Cornwall. Tel: 01326 561885

Rogers Tackle Shop, Higher Bore St, Bodmin, Cornwall. Tel: 01208 78006

Saltash Tackle & Bait, 9, Culver Rd, Saltash, PL12 4DW, Cornwall. Tel: 01752 415437

Sandies Tackle, 7 Penryn St, Redruth, Cornwall. Tel: 01209 214877

Sling Your Hook, 5a Beach Parade, Beach Rd, Newquay, Cornwall. Tel: 01637 852101

The Tackle Box, 1, Swanpool St, Falmouth, TR11 3HU, Cornwall. Tel: 01326 315849

Vennings, Fore S,t Tintage,l Cornwall. Tel: 01840 770212

WSB Tackle Ltd, Treleigh Industrial Estate, Jon Davey Drive, Redruth, Cornwall. Tel: 01209 215000

Waterfront Fishing & Shooting, The Wharf, Bude, Cornwall. Tel: 01288 359606

West Cornwall Angling, Alexandra Rd, Penzance, Cornwall. Tel: 01736 362363

Whealy Fishy Bait Co, 35 Treskewes Estate, Helston, (Bait Only) Tel: 01326 280069

POLE FISHING
FOR THE BEGINNER

Of all the different methods of fishing I've tried, I haven't found any of them as accurate or as easy as pole fishing. To be able to place your bait and feed to the exact spot, sometimes only inches from an island or group of reeds is what makes pole fishing so productive and fun.

TACKLE NEEDED

A Pole

Poles come in various sizes, from 4 metres (usually called a whip) to poles of 18.5 metres. They also vary dramatically in price as well, this is usually governed by weight and rigidity. The lighter and straighter (no droop at the end) the more expensive they are. I recommend a pole between 11 and 13 metres, stay away from the smaller telescopic ones. Many tackle shops have poles ready assembled for you to handle, make sure you are comfortable with its weight and it feels well balanced. Test that it takes apart smoothly. If possible, get a pole with a spare top section as they enable you to rig up for different species and size of fish.

Pole Rigs

Experienced anglers can make up their own pole rigs but beginners are advised to buy ready-made. There are plenty of quality ready made rigs available for as little as £2.99. These rigs come with a main line with a loop on the end (used to attach the line to the stonfo connector at the tip of your pole). A float with enough shot below it to cock it nicely in the water and a length of lower breaking strain line, which has a spade end hook tied to it. The float and shot can slide down the line and be adjusted accordingly.

Pole Elastic

The elastic that runs through the top sections of your pole cushions the fight of a hooked fish and allows you to play it. Elastics are graded in sizes 1-20.
The following list is a good guide for the beginner:
1. For small roach and perch for example - use a No4 elastic with a 1lb hook length and a 2lb main line.
2. If fishing for small carp and tench or skimmer bream use a No8 or 10 elastic with a 3.5lb main line and 2.5lb hook length.
3. When fishing for carp up to 12lbs use a No16 to 18 elastic, and a main line of 8lb with a 6.5lb hook length.

START TO FISH

Fishing Position

Get your seatbox in position. Ideally, when sitting on the box, your thighs should be in a horizontal position, at right angles to your lower leg. Holding the pole correctly makes it comfortable for long periods and prevents backache. For a right handed person you need to rest the pole across your knees with your left hand supporting it. Put your right forearm along the end of the pole and firmly grip the pole with your right hand. Have close to hand - your bait, landing net, disgorger and anything else you may require for your days fishing. It is important to have your pole roller in the correct location. The pole has to be well balanced in your hands when it leaves the roller - this prevents rig tangles when shipping out.

Start Fishing

You have set up your pole and plumbed your depth - so now you are ready to fish. Make sure you have between 10" and 20" of line between the tip and float. In more windy conditions you may want to lengthen this. Feed your swim with groundbait (if allowed) plus a few bits of your hook bait. This is more accurately done using a pole cup which can be fixed to the end of your pole. Put your bait on the hook and ship out your pole trying to keep your rig in the water as this prevents tangles. Lay the rig on the water lengthways. The shot on the line will pull the line under the water and cock the float.
Enjoy your first pole fishing day!

Keep a record of all your fishing trips with

Log-it

Venue:		Address:			Date:
Peg No:	Start Time:		End Time:	Weather Conditions:	

Species	Weight	Method	Rig set up	Ground Bait	Hook Bait	Time

Venue:		Address:				Date:
Peg No:	Start Time:		End Time:		Weather Conditions:	

Species	Weight	Method	Rig set up	Ground Bait	Hook Bait	Time

Venue:		Address:			Date:
Peg No:	Start Time:		End Time:	Weather Conditions:	

Species	Weight	Method	Rig set up	Ground Bait	Hook Bait	Time

59

COARSE FISHING TERMS

Here is a list of the words most commonly used. This will help anglers new to the sport to understand fishing terms used by other anglers.

BALE ARM: A revolving arm on a fixed spool reel which winds line onto the spool.

BAGGING UP: A term used when an angler is catching really well, or to describe a venue that is fishing well.

BAIT BANDS: These are small rubber bands. They are aimed at securing difficult to hook baits to the hook. They come in various sizes to accommodate the size of the bait.

BAITING NEEDLE: These pull the hair loop through the bait. They have a mechanism for attaching to the loop whether it is like a small hook, or a pivot that hooks over the loop. The needle is then drawn back through the bait taking the loop and hair with it.

BARBLESS: A type of hook without sharp barbs to help retain bait and fish. Barbed hooks are banned from most fisheries.

BIN LIDS: A slang term for large bream.

BITE ALARMS: These are electronic sensors that detect the movement of line caused by the fish. They usually have an audible alarm or light to alert the angler.

BIVIES: These are domed tents with an opening at the front providing a shelter from the elements.

BOILIES: These are generally hard balls of bait that are primarily designed as a carp bait.

BREAD PUNCH: A bread punch has a circular 'punch' at the end which is pushed down onto a slice of bread and cuts a small piece out which is placed on the hook. There are many different sizes of punches for different hook sizes.

BREAKING STRAIN: The amount of pressure a line will take before snapping.

BUMPED OFF: This term is used by pole anglers, whereby through the use of heavy tactics the fish once hooked is bumped off. This happens when the fish is not big enough to expand the elastic fully.

CASTERS: The chrysalis form of a maggot.

DEADBAITING: The use of dead fish for catching predatory fish such pike, perch, and eels.

DISGORGER: A long device to help remove the hook from a fish's mouth. Always have one with you.

FOUL HOOKED: A fish that has been hooked anywhere else on the body apart from the mouth.

GROUNDBAIT: A dry mixture intended to be thrown into the water to attract fish. Usually consists of bread crumb, crushed biscuit, crushed hemp or other ingredients.

HAIR RIG: A hair rig is generally a piece of line that extends beyond the point of the shank of the hook. On the end of the length of line is a small loop.

HOOKLENGTH: A short length of line, of lesser breaking strength than the mainline, to which the hook is tied. It is used to make it less likely to be detected by the fish. It also ensures that if the line is snapped by a fish, the angler would not then lose the float / swim feeder / leger and all the other shot

LEGERING: Bait held on the bottom by means of a weight or feeder.

LOOSEFEED: Small offerings of loose bait, such as maggots or sweetcorn, which are thrown into the water to keep the fish interested in the area you are fishing.

LINE BITES: False indications of bites usually caused by fish brushing against the line.

LURES: Artificial fish, used to tempt predators such as pike and zander.

MARGIN: This is an area nearest the bank, that has a shallower depth than that of the main water.

MATCH FISHING: A competitive form of coarse fishing which involves people drawing out a random peg (a place to fish), and then trying to catch as many fish as possible within the allotted time. Usually the winner will be the one with the greatest weight of fish caught.

PEG: A peg is a pre defined fishing area. Venues are split up into evenly spaced fishing zones which are often marked with a wooden peg or marker.

PINKIES: The larvae of the green bottle fly. Small, very lively and great as a loosefeed on stillwaters and canals or as a hookbait for smaller fish.

PLUMMET: A device used for determining the depth of the water in which you are fishing.

POLE: A pole is constructed from very advanced carbon combinations and comes in various sizes, weight and prices.

POLE RIG: These are lengths of line that have the float, weights and a hook attached.

QUIVER TIP: A special type of rod used to detect bites when ledgering. It has a sensitive tip that curves over when the angler has a bite. Quiver tips vary in strength and stiffness which can be changed according to the weather conditions.

SNAGS: Features in your swim that are likely to cause you problems They can also be fish holding features such as lilies, overhanging trees, sunken branches. A place to avoid once a fish is hooked.

SPADE END HOOKS: Spade end hooks have an up-turned flattened piece of metal instead of an eye to which to tie the fishing line.

SPECIMEN: A term given to any fish that is a particularly good size for its species.

STRIKE: To respond to the taking of the bait by pulling the rod in an upwards or sideways motion to hook the fish.

SWIM: The area of water where you are fishing.

Tackle: A term used to refer to any fishing equipment (photo tackle)

TEST CURVE: The test curve is the time and weight needed to make the tip bend 90 degrees from the rod butt. Each rod has a test curve with those being used for specimen fish such as carp having a greater test curve than a general coarse rod.

TROTTING: Allowing a float to travel at the speed of the current.

WHIP: This is a scaled down version of a pole.

I N D E X

If you know of a fishery that is not included in this guide or you want to update an existing venue. Please fill in the form below.

Fishery Name

Fishery Address

Post code

Contact Name

Telephone No

| Adult Day Ticket Price | £ | concession OAP'S | £ |

Fish species and approximate weights

Brief Description

Rules / Bans

Facilities

Accommodation

Number of Lakes

Please e-mail or post a colour photo for inclusion in the next publication.

New Fishery ☐

Please return this form to:
Arc Publishing
166 Knowle Lane,
Bents Green,
Sheffield, S11 9SJ.
Fax: (0114) 2352994

Update to Fishery ☐

New Fishery / Fishery Update Form

Readers Special Offer